Sharing Books From Birth

Welcome to Practical Parenting Books

It's never too early to introduce your child to books. It's wonderful to see your baby gazing intently at a cloth book; your toddler poring over a favourite picture; or your older child listening quietly to a story. And you are your child's favourite storyteller, so have fun together while you're reading – use silly voices, linger over the pictures and leave pauses for joining in.

In *Tiny Trumpet Plays Hide and Seek*, kind Tiny searches for his baby sister's lost teddy. Have fun turning the flip-flaps to discover the hidden surprises, then join in Tiny's game and spot all his jungle friends. Maybe you could hide some soft toys at home for your own game of hide and seek!

Books open doors to other worlds, so take a few minutes out of your busy day to cuddle up close and lose yourselves in a story. Your child will love it – and so will you.

Jane & Clare

Jane Kemp   Clare Walters

P.S. Look out, too, for *Tiny Trumpet, Ten Sleepy Bunnies* and *Good Luck, Mrs Duck!* the companion books in this age range, and all the other great books in the Practical Parenting™ series.

AGE
2-3

This edition produced for The Book People Ltd, Hall Wood Avenue, Haydock, St Helens WA11 9UL

First published in Great Britain
by HarperCollins Publishers Ltd in 2001

1 3 5 7 9 10 8 6 4 2
ISBN: 0-00-764679-8

Practical Parenting™ is an IPC trademark © IPC Media 2001

Text copyright © Jane Kemp and Clare Walters 2001
Illustrations copyright © Mandy Stanley 2001

The Practical Parenting™/HarperCollins pre-school book series has been created by Jane Kemp and Clare Walters. The Practical Parenting™ imprimatur is used with permission by IPC Media.

A CIP catalogue record for this title is available from the British Library.

The HarperCollins website address is: www.fireandwater.com

Manufactured in China by Imago

Practical Parenting™ is published monthly by IPC Media.
To get Practical Parenting™ delivered to your door every month ring the subscriptions hotline on 01444 445555 or the credit card hotline (UK orders only) on 01622 778778

Tiny Trumpet
Plays Hide and Seek

Written by Jane Kemp and Clare Walters

Illustrated by Mandy Stanley

TED SMART

A very loud noise was shaking the jungle:
"Wha, whaa, WHAAA!" Baby Trumpet was crying.

"Baby's lost her teddy," explained Mum.

"I'll help look for it!" said Tiny Trumpet. And off he went.

First Tiny looked by the lake.

"Is Baby's teddy behind these rocks?"

"No! It's me, Hugo."

Tiny and Hugo searched among the bushes.

"Is Baby's teddy in these flowers?"

The three friends went into the forest.
"Is Baby's teddy among these trees?"

"No! It's me, Lofty."

Just then, they heard a
rustling noise high in the branches.

Teddy!

Teddy!

Naughty Minnie had hidden Baby's teddy.

"Sorry Baby!" she said.

And Baby Trumpet STOPPED crying.

"Now you can all play," said Dad.

"And I know just the game," shouted Tiny. "HIDE AND SEEK!"

Can YOU find Tiny and his friends?

Sharing Books From Birth to Five

AGE 0-1

AGE 1-2

AGE 2-3

AGE 3-5

ALL £3.99

The Practical Parenting™ books are available from all good bookshops and can be ordered direct from HarperCollins Publishers by ringing 0141 7723200 and through the HarperCollins website: www.fireandwater.com

You can also order any of these titles, with free post and packaging, from the Practical Parenting™ Bookshop on 01326 569339 or send your cheque or postal order together with your name and address to: Practical Parenting™ Bookshop, Freepost, PO Box 11, Falmouth, TR10 9EN.